Penguin

BALLET SHOES

NOEL STREATFEILD

LEVEL

2

RETOLD BY HANNAH DOLAN
ILLUSTRATED BY CAROL JONAS
SERIES EDITOR: SORREL PITTS

PENGUIN BOOKS

UK | USA | Canada | Ireland | Australia
India | New Zealand | South Africa

Penguin Books is part of the Penguin Random House group of companies
whose addresses can be found at global.penguinrandomhouse.com.
www.penguin.co.uk www.puffin.co.uk www.ladybird.co.uk

Ballet Shoes first published by Dent 1936
Published by Puffin Books 1949
New Puffin Books edition published 2015
This Penguin Readers edition published by Penguin Books Ltd 2021
001

Original text written by Noel Streatfeild
Text for Penguin Readers edition adapted by Hannah Dolan
Original copyright © Noel Streatfeild 1936
Text copyright © Penguin Books Ltd, 2021
Illustrated by Carol Jonas
Cover illustration by Olivia Holden
Illustrations copyright © Penguin Books Ltd, 2021

The moral right of the original author has been asserted

Printed and bound in Great Britain by Clays Ltd, Elcograf S.p.A.

The authorized representative in the EEA is Penguin Random House Ireland,
Morrison Chambers, 32 Nassau Street, Dublin D02 YH68.

A CIP catalogue record for this book is available from the British Library

ISBN: 978–0–241–52065–9

All correspondence to:
Penguin Books
Penguin Random House Children's
One Embassy Gardens, 8 Viaduct Gardens,
London SW11 7BW

Contents

People in the story   4

New words   5

Note about the story   6

Before-reading questions   6

Chapter One – Great-Uncle Matthew's fossils   7

Chapter Two – The boarders   11

Chapter Three – The Fossils make a vow   16

Chapter Four – The Children's School
  of Dancing   22

Chapter Five – *The Blue Bird*   25

Chapter Six – Pauline's new dress   30

Chapter Seven – Pauline learns a lesson   36

Chapter Eight – *A Midsummer Night's Dream*   41

Chapter Nine – Pauline's money   45

Chapter Ten – In the history books   48

During-reading questions   56

After-reading questions   58

Exercises   59

Project work   63

Glossary   64

People in the story

Pauline

Petrova

Posy

Sylvia

Gum

Nana

New words

aeroplane

ballet

fossil

necklace

sum

theatre/stage

Note about the story

Noel Streatfeild (1895–1986) came from Sussex, England. She was the second of three sisters. Noel went to a theatre school, and later she began writing children's stories.

Ballet Shoes (1936) was Noel's first book for children. It is the story of three sisters at a dancing school. They learn to dance, **act*** and sing there. Noel remembered many things about her time at theatre school, and she used them in this story.

Later, the girls start working in theatres. Pauline and Petrova get **parts** in a **performance** of William Shakespeare's *A Midsummer Night's Dream*. It is a very famous and funny story about a strange and beautiful world.

Before-reading questions

1 In the story, the Fossil sisters go to a dancing school. What do you know about dancing schools?

2 Look at the "People in the story" on page 4. Choose one of the people in the pictures and write about him or her.

3 Look at the pictures in the story. Choose your favourite one and write about it.

*Definitions of words in **bold** can be found in the glossary on page 64.

CHAPTER ONE

Great-Uncle Matthew's fossils

The Fossil sisters – Pauline, Petrova and Posy – lived on Cromwell Road in London. They lived with Sylvia, Gum's **great-niece**, and Nana. Nana **looked after** the children, and she looked after Sylvia before that.

"Gum" was the children's shorter name for **Great-Uncle** Matthew. The Fossil sisters did not remember Gum, but he was a very important person to them. Many years before, Gum went away, and he never came back. Sylvia and Nana told the girls many stories about him.

Gum liked to travel the world. In every country, he found fossils, and he sent them home. Each room in the house had fossils in it.

One time, Gum went away on a ship. But there was an accident and the ship went under the water. Many people on the ship died, but a baby girl lived.

Nobody knew the baby's name because her parents died. Gum took the baby back to England with him.

In England, Gum tried very hard to find the baby's family, but he could not. Everybody said, "You must give the baby away." But Gum always took interesting things home with him. He carried the baby home to Cromwell Road.

"Sylvia, I have a very special fossil for you!" shouted Gum, at the front door.

"Gum, you're home!" said Sylvia. She was sixteen then. "A baby," she said.

"A baby!" shouted Nana. "Mr Brown, who has time to look after this baby?"

Nana was very angry with Gum. Then the baby made a noise and Nana looked at her for the first time. Nana smiled.

"Which room can we put the baby in?" she asked Sylvia.

The baby had Sylvia's old room, and Nana looked after her. Sometimes Sylvia helped, too. Sylvia chose the name Pauline for the baby.

A year later, Gum got **sick**, and he went into hospital. There, he met a Russian man with a baby. The man was very sick.

"What will I do?" he said to Gum. "I have a baby girl, but I'm going to die."

"I'll look after her," said Gum. "We have one baby at home – we can have two."

Sylvia called the baby Petrova because she wanted her to have a Russian name.

Gum got ready to go away again and Nana spoke to him. "Please don't bring home any more babies. I can only look after two," she said.

Gum was too frightened to carry the third baby home. He sent her with a letter and a pair of ballet shoes. The letter said:

Sylvia,

    This is the daughter of a ballet dancer. The father died, and the mother doesn't have time to look after a baby. I'm going away for a long time. I'll give you money for the next five years.

Your great-uncle,

Matthew

P.S. The baby's name is Posy. I'm sorry, but it's true.

Four months later, Gum sent a box for "The Little Fossils". There were three necklaces inside it.

They did not hear from Gum again for many years.

CHAPTER TWO
The boarders

Sylvia and Nana did not have much money, and Gum did not send any more. Only Pauline got new clothes, because she was the oldest. Then Petrova and Posy wore them after her.

Pauline looked very pretty in her new clothes. She had lots of light hair and big blue eyes.

Petrova looked very different. She had dark brown eyes and black hair.

For a long time, Posy did not have much hair. Then everyone was **surprised** to see her red hair.

Pauline and Petrova started at a school called Cromwell House. They wore dark green coats and hats. One day after school, the children had a big question for Sylvia.

"What's my second name?" asked Pauline. "At school today, they called me 'Pauline Brown'. But my second name isn't Brown because I'm not your family."

"Your second name can be Brown. What other name can I give you?" said Sylvia.

"Gum called us his fossils," said Petrova. "Could 'Fossil' be our second name?"

"That's a great name!" said Pauline. "I'm Pauline Fossil, and you're Petrova Fossil. But Posy can't be called Fossil."

"Why not?" asked Sylvia.

"Because Pauline and I are at school now and Posy is only a baby," said Petrova.

Nana and Posy came into the room. Pauline told Nana about their new second name.

"Fossil," said Nana. "It's a strange name, but it's as good as any other. You can all be called 'Fossil'. Then I can write 'P. Fossil' in your clothes."

Five years later, Posy was six.

"Maybe Posy can start at Cromwell House this year," Nana said to Sylvia.

"Nana," said Sylvia, sadly, "Gum only **left** us money for five years. I can't send Posy to school, and the others must **leave**, too. There isn't much money **left** now. What will we do?"

"Maybe we can have **boarders**," said Nana. "We have lots of rooms here."

"Boarders!" said Sylvia. "Gum won't like that."

"He isn't here," said Nana.

One afternoon after that, someone came to the front door. Petrova opened it, and she saw a man and woman there. Petrova looked past them into the road, and she saw a very nice car.

"Is that yours?" Petrova asked them.

"Yes," answered the man.

"Wow!" said Petrova. She looked at it again. She liked reading books about cars.

"Do you want to look inside it?" asked the man.

"John, we're here to look at rooms, not the car!" said the woman.

But they went to the car and Petrova asked lots of questions about it.

"This is wonderful!" said Petrova. "A car is coming to live here."

"We'll live here, not the car," the man laughed. "We are Mr and Mrs Simpson."

The next boarder was Theo Dane – a dancer. She listened to some music in her room and Posy started dancing beautifully to it.

Two women took the other rooms. They were doctors – Doctor Jakes and Doctor Smith.

One evening, Sylvia read to the girls. Petrova built a toy aeroplane at the same time.

"Sylvia," said Pauline, "will we like the boarders?"

"I won't," said Petrova. "Houses are for families, not boarders."

CHAPTER THREE
The Fossils make a vow

Pauline was sick one day. Nana was out for a walk with Petrova and Posy.

Pauline sat in the living room, and she watched the clock. Then the door opened and Doctor Jakes looked in.

"Why are you sitting there, child?" asked Doctor Jakes.

"I'm sick," said Pauline.

"Would you like to sit with me?" asked Doctor Jakes.

Pauline was happy to go into the doctor's room. She was surprised to see books everywhere.

"You like reading a lot!" said Pauline.

"I do. The 'Doctor' in my name means 'teacher'.

I teach people about books," said Doctor Jakes. "Are you away from school today because you are sick?"

"We don't go to school now," said Pauline. "We have no money left from Gum."

"Who's Gum?" asked Doctor Jakes.

"He's Sylvia's Great-Uncle Matthew," said Pauline. "We girls have no family. Our second name is 'Fossil'."

"It's wonderful to choose your own name," said Doctor Jakes. "Maybe you'll make the name 'Fossil' very important one day. Maybe I'll read your name in **history** books."

Later, Pauline told Petrova and Posy about her afternoon with Doctor Jakes.

"Could we put our name in history books?" Pauline asked them.

"Yes! Let's make a **vow** to put 'Fossil' in history books," said Petrova.

"We three Fossils," Pauline said, "**vow** to put our names in history books."

"We vow," said Petrova and Posy.

"Let's always make this vow on our birthdays," said Pauline.

"Yes," said Petrova. "It'll make our birthdays very special."

One day, Doctor Jakes and Doctor Smith spoke to Sylvia.

"We would like to teach the children, but we don't want you to pay us any money," said Doctor Jakes.

"No money?" said Sylvia. "Why?"

"We'll enjoy teaching them, and we want to help you," said Doctor Jakes.

"Pauline likes reading with Doctor Jakes, and Petrova is good at sums. I can give her lessons in those," said Doctor Smith.

"You're very kind. Thank you!" said Sylvia.

"Wonderful. We'll start tomorrow," said the doctors.

After dinner that evening, Theo Dane spoke to Sylvia.

"I teach at The Children's School of Dancing," she said. "It's Madame Fidolia's school — she's a famous Russian dancer. I spoke to Madame Fidolia about your girls. She'll have them at her school and you don't have to pay her. The girls can pay her later. From age twelve, they can get dancing work and make money."

"They're children. They can't work!" said Sylvia.

"Why not?" said Theo. "Posy is a great dancer. Pauline is very pretty, and she can dance, too. They have no family to help them with money."

"They have me," said Sylvia.

"Yes, but they could also make their own money," said Theo.

Sylvia asked Nana and the two doctors to come into the room, and she told them about the dancing school.

"Let's try it," Nana said, quickly.

"Nana!" said Sylvia. She was very surprised.

"Posy and Pauline are wonderful dancers," said Nana. "Petrova isn't very good at dancing, but she can learn."

"What do you think?" Sylvia asked the doctors.

"You have problems with money," said Doctor Jakes. "Send the children to dancing school, and we'll teach them here, too."

Sylvia took the girls to The Children's School of Dancing. Madame Fidolia was in a classroom with twenty little girls in blue dresses.

"You dance with them," Madame Fidolia said to the Fossils.

Pauline looked at Sylvia, then she started dancing to the music. Petrova did the same, but she danced very badly. Posy danced beautifully.

"You can stop now," said Madame. "You'll start your lessons here on Monday."

CHAPTER FOUR

The Children's School of Dancing

The Fossils started working very hard. At nine o'clock, they began school lessons with the doctors, and they only stopped for ten minutes for milk. At twelve o'clock, they had lunch and then they went for a walk. At four o'clock, they went to the dancing school.

There, the girls danced for an hour in blue dresses, then they changed into white ballet dresses.

On Saturday mornings, the girls had more dancing classes, and singing and **acting** classes, too. Posy

was the best dancer and Pauline did well in the acting classes. Nobody was very good at singing.

One day, Madame Fidolia asked Posy to dance for her. Then she looked at Posy's feet and she smiled. She asked all the other girls to look at Posy's feet, too.

On the bus home, Pauline and Petrova laughed at Posy. "Posy Pretty Feet!" they called her. Posy started crying.

"Stop it, you two!" said Nana.

Pauline laughed. "Have you got pretty feet, Nana?" she asked.

"My feet aren't pretty, but they're fine for me," said Nana. "I don't want to be a ballet dancer."

They all thought about Nana in ballet shoes and could not stop laughing. After that, Pauline and Petrova forgot to call Posy "Pretty Feet" again.

In December, the dancing school closed for Christmas. At home, Mr and Mrs Simpson helped the children. Together they made paper rings. The doctors brought in a beautiful Christmas tree and Cook made Christmas food in the kitchen.

The children could not remember a better Christmas Day. Everyone ate a wonderful lunch together, and they played games all afternoon.

At the end of the day, Pauline, Petrova and Posy were sad because it was the end of Christmas. Then, before bed, some singers came to the window, and they sang Christmas songs. The girls went to bed happily after that.

CHAPTER FIVE
The Blue Bird

Pauline and Posy loved the spring **term** at The Children's School of Dancing, but Petrova did not.

Madame Fidolia started to give Posy special lessons. Posy danced everywhere.

"Stop dancing, Posy!" said Pauline one day at the train station. "People are looking at us."

"But I thought of a dance, and I wanted to try it," said Posy.

"Do it at home!" said Petrova.

Dancing was more important to Posy than anything in the world. She did not dance in the train station because she wanted people to look at her – she danced because she loved it.

Pauline enjoyed acting classes the most, but Petrova did not like any of her classes.

She could not talk to her sisters about it. But Petrova could talk to Mr Simpson. He thought the same as Petrova about dancing – it was stupid, and cars were more important.

On Sunday afternoons, Petrova often looked at Mr Simpson's car with him. They went under the car and Petrova got very dirty. She loved it.

One evening, Mr Simpson told Petrova something.

"I bought a **garage**, Petrova," he said. "Would you like to help me there on Sunday afternoons?"

"Yes!" said Petrova.

After that, Petrova did not think about her dancing classes as much. Her time with Mr Simpson at the garage was more important.

One morning before the summer term, Madame Fidolia spoke to all of her students.

"Everyone is going to be in a **performance** of *The Blue Bird* this term. It is an important performance because we will use the money from it to help a children's hospital," she said. "*The Blue Bird* is about a boy called Tyltyl and a girl called Mytyl. Pauline will be Tyltyl and Petrova will be Mytyl because they are sisters. They can learn the **parts** together quickly."

Petrova learned her words, but acting them was very difficult for her. Doctor Jakes helped her. She taught Petrova to understand Mytyl, and Petrova began to **act** her part well.

On the day of the performance, Theo met Pauline and Petrova at the theatre, and she took them down to the stage. The girls could not speak because they were too frightened.

The music started and the performance began. After her first three sentences, Pauline started to enjoy it. Petrova did not say her first words right, but then she got better.

After the performance, the girls went home, and they had a wonderful tea. Mr and Mrs Simpson, Doctor Jakes and Doctor Smith, Cook and Sylvia were all at the performance, and everyone wanted to talk about it.

"The performance was wonderful. I cried!" said Cook.

"You did very well, Petrova," said Doctor Jakes. "Acting is easy for Pauline, but it isn't for you."

After tea, Sylvia had a **surprise** for the children.

"We're going on holiday to Sussex in August," she said with a big smile.

The news of the holiday came at the end of a very special day.

CHAPTER SIX
Pauline's new dress

The Fossils had a wonderful holiday in Sussex. They did not have a lot of money, but they did not need much. Each morning, they found a quiet place on the beach and danced there. Then they played on the beach or went for long walks.

Cromwell Road looked very grey to them after their holiday. But the girls did not think much about it because the autumn term at the dancing school began the next day.

Pauline had her twelfth birthday that term. At twelve years old, she could get acting and dancing work and make money. One day, Pauline's teacher, Miss Jay, wanted to speak to her.

"I want to see you here at eleven o'clock tomorrow morning, Pauline," said Miss Jay. "Wear a nice dress. I'm taking you to a theatre. You will **audition** for a job."

At home, Nana took Pauline's best dress out of the cupboard.

"You can't wear that!" shouted Nana. "It's too small. You can wear your blue dancing school dress."

"I can't, Nana!" said Pauline.

"She can't go in her school dress," said Petrova.

"No," said Posy. "No one auditions in school dresses."

31

"What can I do?" said Nana. "We don't have money for a new dress."

"We have our necklaces from Gum," said Petrova. "We could get money for them."

Nana looked at the girls. "Let's try that," she said. "We'll take the necklaces to a shop in the morning."

But at dinner, Mr Simpson had a better plan.

"I'll pay you for the necklaces," he said. "Pauline can buy them back later with the money from her job."

Everyone was very happy with Mr Simpson's plan.

Mr Simpson drove Nana and Pauline to the shop, and they bought a beautiful black dress. Then Mr Simpson drove them to the school.

A girl called Winifred was there to audition, too. She wore an ugly brown dress.

"What a nice dress!" Winifred said quietly to Pauline. "Mine is too small."

"I only bought mine this morning," Pauline told her. "My friend paid for it. Don't tell anyone."

"We're going to audition for Alice," said Winifred.

"In Wonderland?" asked Pauline. "I want to be Alice."

"Me too," said Winifred. "And we'll get money. My mother needs it. I have five brothers and sisters."

Miss Jay drove Pauline and Winifred to the theatre, and they went on to the stage. There were eight other girls there, and they all wanted to be Alice.

Pauline heard someone say, "Little girl in black – what's your name?"

"That is Pauline Fossil," said Miss Jay.

Miss Jay spoke to Pauline. "You can begin now. Will you dance or act first?"

"I'll act," said Pauline.

Pauline acted a part from William Shakespeare's *A Midsummer Night's Dream*. Then she sang a song and danced. She was very happy to finish.

"I wasn't very good," Pauline said quietly to Winifred.

"You were great!" said Winifred.

Miss Jay told Winifred to audition next. Winifred did a difficult dance, and she sang beautifully. She was much better than Pauline.

The eight other girls auditioned, then Miss Jay spoke to them all. "Pauline will be Alice," she said. Pauline was very surprised.

"But Winifred was better than me!"

"Winifred is one of our best students," said Miss Jay. "But you look better for Alice. Winifred will be your **understudy**. She will learn the part, too. She must be ready to play it because maybe one day you'll be sick."

Winifred started crying. Everybody said nice things to her, but she could not stop. Pauline thought about Winifred's brothers and sisters.

CHAPTER SEVEN
Pauline learns a lesson

Pauline got £4 a week for being "Alice". Sylvia wanted her to keep a lot of her money in the bank, but Pauline was not happy.

"Sylvia," she said one evening, "I don't want to keep my money in the bank. That money is for you!"

Some of Pauline's money also had to go to the dancing school because Sylvia did not pay for Pauline to go there. And Pauline had to buy their necklaces back from Mr Simpson. Pauline wanted Sylvia to have all the other money.

"It's important to have money in the bank," said Sylvia, kindly. "You'll need it one day."

"But *you* need it now!" said Pauline.

Nana listened quietly to Pauline and Sylvia. Later, the children went to bed and Nana did some sums.

She then took the sums to Sylvia.

"I'd like to talk to you about Pauline's money for *Alice in Wonderland*," said Nana.

Sylvia smiled. "Pauline wants me to have too much of it."

"Pauline wants to help you with money," said Nana. "You can take one pound a week from her for the house. Then take one pound for the girls' clothes. Pauline needs a little money because she must buy their necklaces back from Mr Simpson. That leaves some money for the dancing school and some money in the bank."

"Maybe you're right, Nana," said Sylvia.

That night, Sylvia slept well for the first time in many weeks.

Performances of *Alice in Wonderland* began, and Pauline was a wonderful Alice. She was now an important person in the theatre, and everyone was nice to her.

Then, Pauline began to change. She was good on the stage, but she was not very nice behind the stage. Pauline had a special room to get ready in, and Nana and Winifred, the understudy, sat there with her every day. Nana was sorry for Winifred, but Pauline was not. She started asking Winifred to do things for her.

"Is there something wrong with your arms and legs, Pauline?" Nana asked her.

"I'm giving Winifred something to do!" said Pauline.

Pauline also started leaving some of her clothes on the stage after performances. Mr French, the theatre **manager**, was not happy.

"Pauline, please put your clothes in your room after a performance," he said.

"No!" Pauline shouted, and she walked quickly away to her room.

She heard someone at the door and Nana answered it. It was Mr French.

"Pauline, you must get your clothes from the stage now, please," he said.

Pauline was very angry. "You get them!" she shouted.

Mr French and Nana were very surprised.

"Is the understudy here?" asked Mr French.

Winifred came to the door. "You'll be Alice tomorrow," Mr French told her. "Pauline will be your understudy."

At home that night, Pauline ran to the bathroom. She lay down on the floor, and she cried very hard.

Nana put the other children to bed, then she went to the bathroom.

"Come out now, Pauline," said Nana. "You learned an important lesson today. You're not special. You were Alice today, but Winifred can be Alice tomorrow. Winifred is only Alice for one performance, then you'll be Alice again. Let's be happy for Winifred."

The next day, Pauline went to the theatre with Nana, and she sat quietly in her room. Winifred was very good in the performance, and Pauline was happy for her.

CHAPTER EIGHT
A Midsummer Night's Dream

Petrova was nearly twelve, and she could start working soon, too. She tried very hard at the dancing school, but she never liked dancing any better.

Petrova's favourite day of the week was Sunday. Then, she and Mr Simpson went to the garage and worked on cars all afternoon. Sometimes, Mr Simpson and Petrova saw aeroplanes, too. Petrova planned to fly an aeroplane one day.

On Petrova's birthday in August, Mr and Mrs Simpson took the children, Nana, Sylvia and Cook on a picnic.

After lunch, the girls made their vow. They made it on every one of their birthdays.

"Let's add something to our vow about making money to help Sylvia. We three Fossils," said Pauline, importantly, "vow to put our names in history books and make money for Sylvia."

"We vow," said Petrova and Posy together.

Back at home, there was a letter from Miss Jay for Pauline and Petrova. She wanted them to audition for parts in *A Midsummer Night's Dream* the next day.

Pauline auditioned and got the part of Peaseblossom. Petrova was very surprised to get the part of Mustard-seed.

Petrova often could not say her words right, and sometimes the people at the theatre got angry with her. But Doctor Jakes helped her again. Mustard-seed did not have many words to learn, and sometimes Petrova got time to read her book about aeroplanes at the theatre.

One day, Pauline and Petrova got a big surprise. Pease-blossom and Mustard-seed had to learn to fly across the stage!

The first night of the performance came, and everyone at home wanted to see it.

In bed that night, Pauline, Petrova and Posy talked about the performance.

"Do you like acting now, Petrova?" asked Pauline.

Petrova liked flying on the stage, but she liked reading about aeroplanes more. "No, not very much," she said.

"The dancers in the big parts were very good," said Pauline.

"I could dance their parts better than them," said Posy. "Look!"

Posy started dancing on her bed.

"That's not right," said Pauline. "They did this." Pauline got up on her bed and she danced, too. But she flew off her bed and on to the floor. Nana heard the loud noise and she opened the bedroom door.

"Get into bed, Pauline," said Nana. "Stop dancing and start sleeping!"

CHAPTER NINE

Pauline's money

Pauline and Petrova each got £3 a week for their parts in *A Midsummer Night's Dream*.

"Sylvia," said Pauline, one day, "I want to give you more money and keep a little for me, too. I want to go to theatres sometimes and watch other performances."

"Theatre tickets are a stupid thing to buy," said Petrova. "I'd like lots of books."

"Of course you can have a little money, Pauline," said Sylvia, "but I don't want any more for the house. You can keep that money in the bank."

"I don't want to put any more money in the bank!" shouted Pauline.

"It's important for a child to have money in the bank," said Sylvia.

"But I'm not a child," said Pauline, "I'm fourteen now. I made that money and I'd like us all to have some of it now."

Posy looked at Sylvia. "That's a good plan," she said.

"I like it, too," said Nana. "Pauline is very good at acting. Maybe she'll make a lot of money one day. Maybe she won't need all of that money in the bank."

Six weeks later, *A Midsummer Night's Dream* finished and Pauline got a big part in a different Shakespeare performance. Everyone loved her in it.

One day, a man asked Pauline to audition for a part in a film about Charles the Second. Mr Simpson drove Sylvia and Pauline to a big building outside London. Pauline had to act in front of lots of cameras and it was very strange.

Many months later, Pauline got a letter about the film. She got the part! The film people paid her £10 a day.

Acting in front of cameras was very different to acting in the theatre. Pauline learned quickly, but she liked acting in the theatre better.

In the history books

In the spring term, Posy came home from the dancing school, and she started crying.

"Madame is sick!" she said. "She's going to a hospital in Switzerland. She'll be there for months!"

"That's very bad for Madame," said Sylvia.

Posy looked at Sylvia. "It's very bad for me! What about my dancing?" she asked, angrily.

Sylvia was surprised at Posy, but Pauline and Petrova understood her.

"Posy's the best dancer at the dancing school. Only Madame can teach her," said Pauline.

"You're right," said Petrova. "What will happen to Posy now?"

Posy started being difficult at the dancing school

and the teachers got angry with her. Theo and the other teachers wanted Posy to go to the normal dancing classes, but Posy did not want to.

Theo was not happy with Posy, but she could not tell Sylvia. Sylvia had many other things to think about. Then Theo asked Pauline to talk to Posy.

"Posy, a famous ballet dancer called Manoff is in London," said Pauline, one night.

"I heard about that!" said Posy.

"Would you like to see him dance?" asked Pauline.

"Yes, more than anything!" said Posy.

"I've got two pounds from my film money," Pauline told her. "I'll take you, but you must go to your dance classes with Theo."

Posy was much nicer at the dancing school after that, and Pauline bought two tickets for the ballet. Manoff's performance was wonderful.

That evening, Posy came back to the house, and she got into bed quietly.

"What's the matter, Posy?" asked Pauline.

"I must learn from Manoff," answered Posy.

"But he teaches in Czechoslovakia," said Pauline.

The next morning, Posy did not go to her lessons with Doctor Jakes and Doctor Smith. She was not at home, but nobody saw her leave.

"She'll come back," the doctors told Pauline and Petrova. "Let's not tell Sylvia and Nana until later."

Then someone came to the front door. It was a man called Mr Reubens. He wanted to talk to Sylvia and Pauline. They went into the living room, and Petrova waited by the front door for Posy. After some time, Pauline came out and she sat with Petrova.

"Mr Reubens works in films," said Pauline. "He saw me in the film about Charles the Second. He wants me to move to Hollywood and make more films. But I don't want to go."

"Why not?" asked Petrova.

"I want to act in theatres, not in films," said Pauline.

"How much will they pay you?" asked Petrova.

"A hundred pounds a week," answered Pauline.

Petrova was very surprised. "A hundred pounds!"

"Maybe more," said Pauline. "But I don't want to go. It's for five years."

Posy walked through the door.

"Posy!" Pauline and Petrova shouted together. "Where did you go?"

"He'll take me!" said Posy, happily.

"Who?" asked Petrova.

"Manoff!" said Posy. "I went to the theatre this morning and Manoff was there. I asked him to watch me dance and he said yes. At the end, he said, 'You will come to my dancing school and I will make you a great ballet dancer!'"

"Posy, Sylvia doesn't have the money to send you there," said Petrova.

"But I can pay! I'll go to Hollywood and make films. I'll tell Sylvia and Mr Reubens now," said Pauline. "Posy, you can go to Czechoslovakia with Nana, and I can go to Hollywood with Sylvia."

Petrova looked sad. "What about me?" she asked.

"You must stay here and put our name in history books!" said Posy.

"How can I do that?" asked Petrova.

"By flying aeroplanes, of course," said Posy.

The Fossils were very surprised to see the door open again and an old man walk in. He had grey hair and a big bag in one hand. He put the bag on the floor. The girls looked at him quietly, then they walked slowly towards him.

"Are you Gum?" Pauline asked.

"Of course," he answered. "Who are you?"

"We're Pauline, Petrova and Posy," said Petrova.

"You were babies!" Gum said.

Posy held his arm. "You were away for a long time," she said.

"Was I? The years went quickly," Gum said. "But I want to hear about you."

They all sat by the door. The girls told Gum about Pauline and Posy's news.

Gum looked at Petrova, "Everyone is leaving," he said. "But you're not. How can I help you?"

"She likes flying and cars," said Posy.

"Very good," said Gum. "You can study aeroplanes."

Petrova looked very happy. "I will like that," she said.

"We're all going to do very different things," said Pauline.

"In different places!" added Posy.

Petrova looked at her sisters and smiled. "We can do anything."

During-reading questions

1 Who is Gum? What does he like to do?
2 Where does Gum find the first baby?
3 Why does Sylvia call the second baby Petrova?

1 Pauline and Petrova do not want their second name to be "Brown". Why?
2 Sylvia cannot send Posy to school, and Pauline and Petrova must leave school. Why?
3 Why is Petrova happy about Mr and Mrs Simpson living at her house?

1 Why are there lots of books in Doctor Jakes' room?
2 What do the children vow to do?
3 Three people speak to Sylvia about the children in this chapter. Who are they? How do they want to help the children?

1 What classes do the children have at The Children's School of Dancing?
2 Why does Madame Fidolia smile at Posy's feet, do you think?
3 The children and Nana cannot stop laughing on the bus home. Why?

CHAPTER FIVE

1 What is more important to Petrova than dancing?
2 Why do Pauline and Petrova get their parts in *The Blue Bird*?
3 How does Doctor Jakes help Petrova?

CHAPTER SIX

1 What can Pauline do after her twelfth birthday?
2 What does Mr Simpson buy from the children? Why?
3 Why is Pauline surprised to get the part of Alice?

CHAPTER SEVEN

1 Why does some of Pauline's money have to go to the dancing school?
2 Why does Nana ask, "Is there something wrong with your arms and legs, Pauline?"
3 What important lesson does Pauline learn in this chapter?

CHAPTER EIGHT

1 What words do the children add to their vow?
2 What does Petrova take to read at the theatre?
3 What big surprise do Pauline and Petrova get at the theatre in this chapter?

CHAPTER NINE

1 What does Pauline want a little bit of money for?
2 Look at the picture on page 47. Pauline now has a part in a film. Is she playing a boy or a girl, do you think? Does he or she look rich or poor?
3 What does Pauline think is strange about acting in films?

1 Who is Manoff?
2 Where does Mr Reubens want Pauline to go?
3 Why does Gum say "You were babies!"?

After-reading questions

1 In Chapter Two, Petrova says, "Houses are for families, not boarders." What does Petrova think about the boarders later in the book, do you think?
2 Why does Posy dance at the train station in Chapter Five?
3 Sylvia tells Pauline, "It's important to have money in the bank." Why is this important in the story? What does Pauline think? What do you think?
4 Look at "Before-reading question 2". What new things do you know about this person now?
5 At the end of the story, the Fossil sisters are going to do different things in different places. What are they all going to do? Which of these do you like the best?

Exercises

1 **Are these sentences *true* or *false*? Write the correct answers in your notebook.**

1   The Fossil sisters remember Gum well. ....*false*...........
2   Gum and Pauline were in an accident on a ship.
3   Gum met a Russian woman with a baby.
4   Nana chose the name Petrova for the second baby.
5   Posy's mother was a ballet dancer.
6   Gum sent a box with three pencils in it.

2 **Write the opposite of the word in your notebook.**

1   oldest .....*youngest*............
2   pretty
3   light
4   strange
5   laugh
6   sick

CHAPTER FOUR

3 **Write the correct question word. Then answer the questions in your notebook.**

What	Why	When	Who
	How	Which	

1 ....*When*............ did the girls begin school lessons with the doctors? ...*At nine o'clock*...

2 .... long did the girls dance in blue dresses for?

3 .... was very good at acting?

4 .... boarders brought a beautiful Christmas tree to the house?

5 .... did everyone do all Christmas afternoon?

6 .... were the children sad at the end of the day?

4 **Match the two parts of the sentences in your notebook.**
Example: 1 − c

1 Dancing was more important to Posy   **a** with the money from her job.

2 Petrova learned all her words   **b** and she sang beautifully.

3 The news of the holiday came   **c** than anything in the world.

4 Pauline can buy the necklaces back later   **d** at the end of a very special day.

5 There were eight other girls there,   **e** but acting them was very difficult for her.

6 Winifred did a difficult dance,   **f** and they all wanted to be Alice.

5 Complete these sentences in your notebook, using the infinitives from the box.

to keep	to finish	to do	to speak
	to change	to have	

1 One day, Pauline's teacher, Miss Jay, wanted ....*to speak*...... to her.

2 Pauline was very happy .... her audition.

3 "I don't want .... my money in the bank," said Pauline.

4 "Pauline wants me .... too much of it," said Sylvia.

5 Pauline began .... She was good on the stage, but she was not very nice behind the stage.

6 Pauline started asking Winifred .... things for her.

CHAPTER EIGHT

6 Complete these sentences in your notebook, using the words from the box.

vow	surprise	auditioned	parts
	performance	aeroplane	

1 Petrova planned to fly an ......*aeroplane*........ one day.

2 The girls made their .... on every one of their birthdays.

3 Pauline .... and got the part of Pease-blossom.

4 One day, Pauline and Petrova got a big ....

5 In bed that night, Pauline, Petrova and Posy talked about the ....

6 "I could dance their .... better than them," said Posy.

7 **Who said this? Write the correct names in your notebook.**

1 "Theatre tickets are a stupid thing to buy." ....*Petrova*.........

2 "But I'm not a child."

3 "I must learn from Manoff."

4 "I want to act in theatres, not in films."

5 "She likes flying and cars."

6 "We can do anything."

Pauline   Petrova   Posy

CHAPTER TEN

8 **Order the words to make sentences in your notebook.**

1 at / was / Posy. / Sylvia / surprised

   Sylvia was surprised at Posy.

2 many / had / about. / other / things / to / Sylvia / think

3 wonderful. / was / Manoff's / performance

4 at / Posy / leave. / not / home, / but / saw / was / her / nobody

5 had / one / hair / grey / hand. / bag / and / big / a / He / in

6 her / Petrova / at / sisters / smiled. / and / looked

9 **Write the past tense of these irregular verbs in your notebook.**

1 They ....*wore*............ (**wear**) dark green coats and hats.

2 The doctors .... (**bring**) in a beautiful Christmas tree.

3 Doctor Jakes .... (**teach**) Petrova to understand Mytyl.

4 Pauline .... (**think**) about Winifred's brothers and sisters.

5 Pauline........... (**fly**) off her bed and on to the floor.

6 Pauline .... (**buy**) two tickets for the ballet.

Project work

1 The children make their vows every year on their birthdays. Write your own vow.

2 You are Pauline, Petrova or Posy. Write a diary of your day at The Children's School of Dancing.

3 Make a poster for The Children's School of Dancing. Write about Madame Fidolia and the classes at the school.

4 You are one of the Fossil sisters after the end of the story. Write a letter to one of your sisters. Tell them about your new life and ask about their new life.

5 Choose an important part of the story and act it with friends. Think about the different parts, their words and how to act them.

6 Look online. Find out five things about Noel Streatfeild.

An answer key for all questions and exercises can be found at **www.penguinreaders.co.uk**

Glossary

act (v.); **acting** (n.)
to play a *part* in a *performance*.
This is *acting*.

audition (v.)
You *act* or dance in front of some
people. Then they say, "You
can/cannot have a *part* in our
performance." This is an *audition*.

boarder (n.)
an old word. A *boarder* lives in your
house and pays you every week or
every month.

garage (n.)
A *garage* is a place for cars.

great-niece (n.)
Your *great-niece* is the granddaughter
of your brother or sister.

great-uncle (n.)
Your *great-uncle* is the brother of
your grandmother or grandfather.

history (n.)
History books are books about the
past.

leave (v.); **left** (adj.)
You do not use something. You *leave*
it for other people and they can use
it. That thing is *left*.

look after (phr. v.)
to help a person, animal or thing

manager (n.)
A *manager* tells other people to
do work.

part (n.)
You *act* a person in a play or film.
This is a *part*. You play a *part* in
a *performance*.

performance (n.)
You *act* or dance in a *performance*.
People watch you.

sick (adj.)
A *sick* person feels bad in their
body. They are not very well.

surprise (n.); **surprised** (adj.)
Something happens and you did
not know about it. You are *surprised*.
This is a *surprise*.

term (n.)
part of a school year. There are
three *terms* in a school year. For
example, the autumn *term* is from
September to December and the
summer *term* is from April to July.

understudy (n.)
Your *understudy* learns your *part*.
Maybe you get *sick*. Then your
understudy acts in your *performance*.

vow (v. and n.)
You *vow* to do something. Then
you must do it. This is a *vow*.